Curriculum Vis

Spelling Book 4

Sarah Lindsay

Curriculum Visions
Spelling

Teacher's Resource Book
There is a Teacher's Resource Book to accompany this Pupil Book.

Dedicated Web Site
There's more information about other great Curriculum Visions resources and a wealth of supporting material available at:
www.CurriculumVisions.com

Author
Sarah Lindsay

Art Director
Duncan McCrae

Senior Designer
Adele Humphries

Editors
Robert Anderson and Gillian Gatehouse

Illustrations
Mark Stacey

Designed and produced by
EARTHSCAPE EDITIONS

Printed in China by
WKT Company Ltd

This product is manufactured from sustainable managed forests. For every tree cut down at least one more is planted.

First published in 2006 by Atlantic Europe Publishing Company Ltd Reprinted June 2006

Text copyright © Sarah Lindsay 2006

The right of Sarah Lindsay to be identified as the author of this work has been asserted by her in accordance with the Copyright, Designs and Patents Act 1988.

Illustrations and design copyright © 2006 Atlantic Europe Publishing Company Ltd

Curriculum Visions Spelling Book 4 A CIP record for this book is available from the British Library.

ISBN-10: 1-86214-513-X
ISBN-13: 978-1-86214-513-9

Contents

Unit 1

less
ness

thoughtless

darkness

careless	darkness	defenceless	craziness
homeless	fitness	meaningless	dizziness
priceless	stillness	senseless	emptiness
worthless	weakness	thoughtless	loneliness

Finding words

A Add **less** or **ness** to each of the words.

1 dark____

2 fit____

3 price____

4 home____

5 weak____

6 care____

B Write a sentence describing the labelled picture at the top of the page.

Using words

When you add a suffix to a word watch out for words ending in **y**!

Read this carefully... it is a useful rule to learn!

If the **y** sounds like **ee** in see, you need to change the **y** to an **i** and then add the suffix.

A Add **ness** to these words ending in **y**.

1 cheeky   **2** greedy   **3** lazy

4 tidy   **5** empty   **6** lovely

B Write a short passage describing something that happened one playtime.

Your passage must include three of the words in the box.

breathless	thoughtless
careless happiness	silliness

Puzzle corner

Spot the correct spelling!
Copy the word that is spelt correctly.

1 somethink   something   somthing

2 stopped   stoped   stoppd

3 diferent   diffrent   different

4 suddenly   sudenly   suddnly

5 thorght   thought   thoght

If you are stuck on a word, check it in a dictionary!

Unit 2

er

dancer

butter

butter	**butch**er	**comput**er	**altogeth**er
gutter	**danc**er	**discov**er	**charact**er
letter	**farm**er	**should**er	**laught**er
litter	**sing**er	**weath**er	**surrend**er

Finding words

A Look at the pictures.
Find the word in the word list and copy it.

1

2

3

4

5

6

B Choose four of the words you have written
and write a word that rhymes with each one.

If I was you I would find a word to rhyme with numbers 1, 3, 4 and 5. Miss out 2 and 6!

Using words

A Each of these pictures shows someone doing a job.

Write the job each of them is doing.
Use the words in the box to help.

soldier   plumber   builder   teacher   gardener   singer

B Write five more jobs that end in **er**.

Puzzle corner

Homophones are words that sound the same but have different spellings.

one   won

> Say the words aloud. They sound the same but have different spellings.

Find the homophone pairs on the puzzle pieces.
Write the pairs you have found.

bough   bow   new   piece   past

bored   days   board

knew   daze   peace

here   hear   passed

7

Unit 3

already
music**al**

also	**coast**al	**accident**al	**arriv**al
always	**magic**al	**autumn**al	**dispos**al
already	**music**al	**electric**al	**natur**al
almost	**physic**al	**fiction**al	**rehears**al

Finding words

Hint… All the words you need to find use **al** as a suffix, not a prefix!

A Copy the sentences.
Fill the gaps with a word from the word list.

1 The castle looked _____.

2 The _____ path on the cliffs looked dangerous.

3 The trees were beginning to look _____.

4 Grandad bought an _____ hedge trimmer.

B Write your own sentence using a different word from the word list.

Using words

Remember **al** can be used either as a suffix or as a prefix.

post + **al** = postal   **al** + so = also

A Look at these root words.
Add the prefix **al** or suffix **al** to make a word.

1 ___magic___   2 ___though___

3 ___ways___   4 ___accident___

5 ___origin___   6 ___ready___

7 ___most___   8 ___together___

B Choose three of the words you have made and write them in a sentence.
Can you write a funny sentence?

Puzzle corner

Rewrite each of these definitions in as few words as possible!

Use only the most important information about each word.

1 gang: a gang is a group of people who hang out and do things together

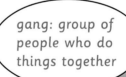

gang: group of people who do things together

2 perimeter: the perimeter is the outside edge of something

3 snow: snow is frozen water that falls from the sky as white flakes, often making things slippery

4 chameleon: a chameleon is a small, lizard-like animal that changes its colour to match the surroundings it is in or the leaf it is sitting on

Unit 4

ment

excitement

advertisement

agreement	**depart**ment	**arrange**ment	**achieve**ment
enjoyment	**equip**ment	**amaze**ment	**advertise**ment
movement	**govern**ment	**excite**ment	**environ**ment
treatment	**punish**ment	**enlarge**ment	**entertain**ment

Finding words

A Match a word from the word list to each picture.

1

2

3

4

5

6

B Underline the suffix in each of the words you have written.

Do you remember... a **suffix** is a group of letters added to a root word?

Using words

A Which of these root words can have the suffix **ment** added to them? Write the new words in your book.

encourage mean enjoy

pay dry

adjust entertain

weak

disappoint sore

B Write three sentences, each with a word you have just made.

Puzzle corner

Copy the sentences and fill each gap with a word from the box.

| two | down | time |

Darren ran _____ the stairs _____ at a _____.

| brother | called | him |

His _____ was chasing _____ because he had _____.

| three | name | times |

him a _____ _____ _____.

Unit 5

verb +

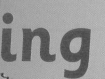

tricking

tricked

check	drag	fix	cancel
knock	knot	relax	grovel
pack	quiz	amuse	quarrel
trick	squat	circle	signal

Finding words

> A **verb** is an action word – it is something that can be done.

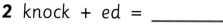

A Finish these word sums.

1 kick + ing = _____

2 knock + ed = _____

3 hit + s = _____

4 trick + ed = _____

5 whisper + ing = _____

6 cook + s = _____

B Write a word sum for each of these words, like this…

screaming = scream + **ing**

1 combing   **2** smashed   **3** gallops

4 filmed   **5** winks   **6** testing

Using words

Watch out... there are a few verbs that don't just have **s**, **ed** and **ing** added!

If a word ends in **e**...
just add **s**, but drop the **e** before adding **ing** or **ed**.

argue   argue**s**   argu**ing**   argu**ed**

If the second to last letter is a single vowel... in most cases just add **s**, but double the last letter before adding **ing** or **ed**.

This doesn't work for words that end in **w**, **x** or **y**!

clap   clap**s**   clapp**ing**   clapp**ed**

Complete the table on the right, but think carefully about the rules!

Verb	+s	+ing	+ed
amuse			
grovel			
scrub			
circle			
travel			

Puzzle corner

Copy the table.
Challenge! Can you put these verbs in the correct column in the table.

catch   thought

saw

caught

see

fall

went

think

go

fell

Past	Present
saw	see

If something has happened in the **past**, it means it has already happened.

If something is happening in the **present** it means it is happening now.

13

Unit 6
hood
ship

friendship   babyhood   partnership   adulthood

membership   brotherhood premiership knighthood

ownership   childhood   sponsorship neighbourhood

township   manhood   relationship likelihood

Finding words

A Add **hood** or **ship** to each of the words.

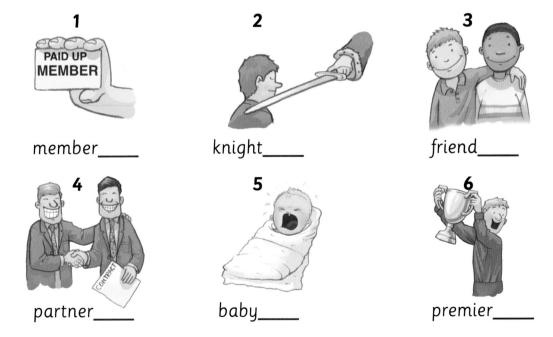

1 member_____

2 knight_____

3 friend_____

4 partner_____

5 baby_____

6 premier_____

B Write a sentence describing the labelled picture at the top of the page.

Using words

A Match the correct **hood** and **ship** words with their definitions.

1	childhood	an award of money towards education
2	scholarship	being likely
3	relationship	a competition
4	likelihood	the way people get along
5	championship	the time of being a child

B Choose two of the words above and write them each in a sentence.

Puzzle corner

Watch out... the first two letters in each word are the same so you need to put the words in alphabetical order using their third letter!

A Put these words in alphabetical order.

1	pond	pocket	police	porridge
2	day	dance	dart	dairy
3	scissors	scarf	school	scout

ABCDEFGHIJKLMNOPQRSTUVWXYZ

B Add one more word to the end of each list of words. The word you have chosen must still be in alphabetical order using its third letter.

Use a dictionary to help!

Unit 7

on
en

ribbon

kitten

button   bitten   lemon   dampen
cotton   kitten   pardon   golden
lesson   mitten   season   heaven
ribbon   rotten   skeleton   oxygen

Finding words

A What am I?

1 I'm a baby cat.
2 I am a fruit that tastes bitter.
3 I'm the bones in a body.
4 I'm used in the cold and don't have fingers.
5 I'm an apology.
6 I keep parts of clothing together.

Shh... You will find the words in the word list!

B Write clues for two more **on** or **en** words. Try them out on a friend.

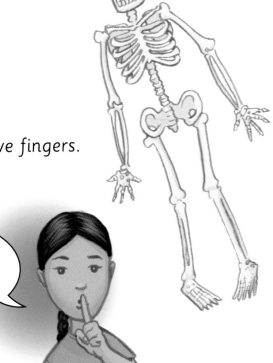

16

Using words

A Add **on** or **en** to make a word.

1 wood___   2 giv___   3 seas___
4 bac___   5 heav___   6 burd___
7 pers___   8 ir___   9 squadr___

Check your words in a dictionary to make sure you've spelt them correctly!

B Choose three of the words you have made and write each of them in a sentence.

Puzzle corner

A Sort the pairs of words into the table.

thick   thicken

dramatise   drama

Noun or adjective	Verb

solid   solidify

fertile   fertilise

B What is added to the noun or adjective to make the verb?

Unit 8
double letters

giggle   kennel

yellow

arrow   flannel   collage   giggle
burrow   kennel   pollute   wriggle
narrow   minnow   shallow   drizzle
sparrow   sunny   yellow   puzzle

Finding words

A What am I?

1 I'm used to wash faces.

2 I'm a very small fish.

3 I'm a type of laugh.

4 A rabbit digs me for its home.

5 I'm a colour.

6 I'm a very light form of rain.

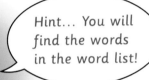
Hint... You will find the words in the word list!

B Write clues for two more double-letter words. Try them out on a friend.

18

Using words

A Complete each word with a pair of double letters from the box.

dd		rr		ss
	ll		tt	

1 co__ect   **2** pa__ot   **3** bu__er
4 a__ress   **5** ke__le   **6** pa__le
7 le__on   **8** lo__y   **9** me__y

B Write a short story. Include as many double-letter words as you can. Underline all the double-letter words you use.

If you use seven words, that's good… fifteen is brilliant… bet you can't use twenty!!

Make a list of double-letter words before you start – it will help.

Puzzle corner

Some words change over time.

PAST
spectacles

PRESENT
glasses

Sort these words into past and present pairs.

wireless   pitcher   jug   dress
satchel   schoolbag
bonnet   frock   radio   hat

Unit 9
ic

enthusiastic

gigantic

artistic   athletic   alphabetic   atmospheric
heroic   fantastic   gigantic   enthusiastic
magnetic   idiotic   horrific   microscopic
robotic   poetic   rhythmic   photographic

Finding words

Look at the pictures.
Find the word in the word list and copy it.

1

2

3
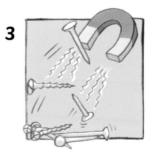

4

5

6

B Write a sentence describing the labelled picture at the top of the page.

Using words

A Copy the sentences and fill the gaps with an **ic** word.

fantastic	allergic	scenic
tragic	frantic	robotic

1 Mum felt _____ when my baby sister got lost.

2 I cried my eyes out at the end of the film, which had a _____ ending.

3 Sophie can't eat peanuts because she is _____ to them.

4 Deano loved his newly decorated room; he thought it looked _____.

5 Kyle loved his new _____ toy.

6 Caroline enjoyed the _____ view; she could even see the sea!

B Choose two more **ic** words and write each of them in a sentence.

Puzzle corner

Copy this passage. Replace each of the **bold** words with a more interesting word or words.

It is very easy to use the same words all the time, but it can make your writing a bit boring! Read the passage below and you will see what I mean! In the first sentence try replacing the word **good** with the word **fantastic**...

Dave and Hannah were having a **good** holiday. Everyday they played by the sea then had a **nice** ice cream. On Tuesday they **got** some postcards for their friends. One evening they had a **nice** meal and then went to a **nice** carnival in the **nice** village. They **got** to bed at 11.00 p.m.!

Unit 10

un
re
non
dis

disbelieve

nondrip

recharge

unaware

unaware	recharge	nondrip	disbelieve
unfair	reconsider	nonexistent	discontinue
unlike	refresh	nonsense	dishonest
unwell	revisit	nonviolent	disregard

Finding words

A Add to each of the root words **un**, **re**, **non** or **dis** to make a new word.

1

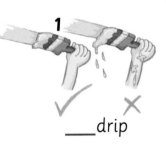

___drip

2

___well

3

___charge

All the words can be found in the word list!

4

___sense

5

___honest

6

___aware

B The root word **charge** can also have one of the prefixes **un**, **non** or **dis** added to it to make another word. Which prefix is it?

Using words

A Write an adventure story.
Include at least six words from the box in your story.
Underline the words.

> **uncertain**   **recapture**   **nonsense**   **disbelieve**
> **unimportant**   **reread**   **nonexistent**   **dismount**

While on holiday you have discovered a map under an old newspaper in a drawer. It gives directions to hidden treasure buried in a cave…

How easy is it for you to find the cave?
Does anyone else come with you?
What do you find?

Puzzle corner

Some words are used for males (masculine words), some are used for females (feminine words).
When the suffix **ess** is added to a word it can change a masculine word to a feminine word.

count

count**ess**

Change these masculine words to make them feminine.

  1 lion   **2** manager   **3** baron
  4 mayor   **5** heir   **6** prince

Unit 11
words ending in *f*

cal*f*

scar*f*

cal*f*	dwar*f*	brie*f*	belie*f*
hal*f*	scar*f*	chie*f*	relie*f*
lea*f*	shel*f*	grie*f*	disbelie*f*
loa*f*	wol*f*	thie*f*	mischie*f*

Finding words

A Copy the sentences.
Fill the gaps with a word from the word list.

1 The warm _____ was delicious.

2 Mia lost her _____ at the playground.

3 The _____ was tracked down by the police.

4 The kitten was full of _____.

B Write your own sentence using
a different word from the word list.

Using words

Watch out... here is an important rule to remember!

When a **suffix** that **begins** with a vowel is added to words ending in a single **f**, the **f** changes to a **v** before the suffix is added.

relie**f** + ed = relie**v**ed

A Add the suffixes to the words ending in **f**.

1 thief + ing = _____   **2** grief + ous = _____

3 relief + ed = _____   **4** grief + ing = _____

5 mischief + ous = _____   **6** shelf + ed = _____

B Choose three of the words you have made and write each one in a sentence.

Puzzle corner

Definition challenge! Write three definitions for each of these words.

The first must have four words, the second three words and the fourth two words.

Like this...

elephant
a big grey animal
a big animal
an animal

1 rain   **2** mouse   **3** tooth

Unit 12

ight

night

light

fight

fight	**l**ight	**fl**ight	**bright**est
might	**n**ight	**sl**ight	**tight**est
right	**t**ight	**bright**	**fright**en
sight	**upt**ight	**fr**ight	**light**en

Finding words

A Look at the pictures.
Find the word in the word list and copy it.

1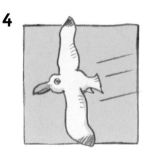

2

3

4

5

6

B Write a sentence describing the labelled picture at the top of the page.

Using words

A Copy and complete the table.

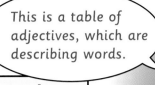

This is a table of adjectives, which are describing words.

Adjective	+er	+est
	lighter	
bright		
		tightest

B Write three sentences, each of which has all the words from one of the rows in the table above.

Puzzle corner

The words below have been put in alphabetical order.
All the words have the same first, second and third letter so they have been put in alphabetical order using their fourth letter.

In each list a word has been missed out.
Add a word, keeping the list in alphabetical order.

1	catapult	catch	caterpillar	
2	penalty	pencil		pentagon
3	scrap		scroll	scrub
4		throw	thrush	thrust

Use a dictionary to help!

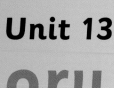

ory
ery
ary

jewellery

story

imaginary

fact**o**ry	deliv**e**ry	diction**a**ry	jewell**e**ry
hist**o**ry	discov**e**ry	Febru**a**ry	machin**e**ry
mem**o**ry	myst**e**ry	libr**a**ry	imagin**a**ry
st**o**ry	nurs**e**ry	prim**a**ry	necess**a**ry

Finding words

A What am I?

1 I'm a piece of fiction.

2 I'm a month.

3 You can look up the meanings of words in me.

4 In me, things are made.

5 You will find young children in me.

6 I decorate bodies.

Hint… You will find the words in the word list!

B Write clues for three more **ory**, **ery** or **ary** words.
Try them out on a friend.

Using words

A Add **ory**, **ery** or **ary** to make a word.

1 mem____	**2** deliv____	**3** jewell____
4 ordin____	**5** libr____	**6** vict____
7 slipp____	**8** bound____	**9** secret____

> If you aren't sure whether to add **ory**, **ery** or **ary** to the letters, check in a dictionary.

B Choose three of the words you have made and write each of them in a sentence.

Puzzle corner

A Sort the pairs of words into the table.

manage   manageable   hopeful   hope

end   endless

Noun or verb	Adjective

supportive   support   reverse   reversible

B List the suffixes added to the noun or verbs in **A** to make adjectives.

Unit 14

ough

drought

trough

c**ough**	b**ought**	d**ough**	dr**ought**
tr**ough**	f**ought**	th**ough**	pl**ough**
r**ough**	n**ough**t	br**ough**t	bor**ough**
t**ough**	th**ough**t	s**ough**t	thor**ough**

Finding words

A Look at the pictures.
Find the word in the word list and copy it.

1

2

3

4

5

6

*Say aloud the words you have written. Do you notice the different sounds the **ough** makes?*

B The word you have written for number **3** rhymes with another word you have written. Which word is it?

Using words

A Copy the sentences and find a rhyming word in the box!

> trough   tough   bough
> brought   dough   thorough   bought

1 **though** rhymes with _____
2 **rough** rhymes with _____
3 **thought** rhymes with _____
4 **borough** rhymes with _____
5 **plough** rhymes with _____
6 **cough** rhymes with _____
7 **fought** rhymes with _____

B Choose three rhyming pairs.
Write three nonsense sentences, each of which includes
both the rhyming words in one of the sentences in **A**.

Puzzle corner

Write a short story about something that happens at a friend's
swimming birthday party.

You must use all the words in the box in your story.
In your story, underline the words from the box.

> brought   great   window   through   thought
> heard   above   suddenly   without   knew

Unit 15
able

washable

agree**able**	accept**able**	advis**able**	believ**able**
bear**able**	adapt**able**	argu**able**	excus**able**
laugh**able**	avoid**able**	excit**able**	lov**able**
washable	prefer**able**	forgiv**able**	reli**able**

Finding words

A Copy the sentences.
Fill the gaps with a word from the word list.

1 The water in the swimming pool was just b_____.

2 The l_____ puppy fell asleep in Wang Ling's lap.

3 The policeman said the accident was a_____.

4 Class 4 are e_____ as they are off to visit a castle.

B Write your own sentence using a different word from the word list.

Using words

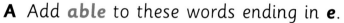

Watch out when you add the **able** suffix to a word ending in one **e**. Usually you need to drop the **e** and then add the suffix.

Read this carefully… it is a useful rule to learn and also works with the **ible** suffix!

A Add **able** to these words ending in **e**.

1 love   2 argue   3 recognise

4 believe   5 inflate   6 adore

B Choose two of the words you have just made and write them both in the same sentence.

This is quite hard to do!

Puzzle corner

Find the two words that make each of these **compound words**.

Do you remember what compound words are? They are words made up of two smaller words.

1 tablecloth = _____ + _____   2 weekend = _____ + _____

3 handbag = _____ + _____   4 cupboard = _____ + _____

5 redhead = _____ + _____   6 database = _____ + _____

7 checkout = _____ + _____   8 anywhere = _____ + _____

Compound words can help you with your spelling. If you find a word difficult to spell look to see if it is a compound word. Then all you have to do is remember the two smaller words!

Unit 16
ible

flexible

incredible

horrible	divisible	collapsible	convertible
possible	edible	responsible	extendible
terrible	flexible	reversible	indigestible
visible	incredible	sensible	irresistible

Finding words

A Look at the pictures.
Find the word in the word list and copy it.

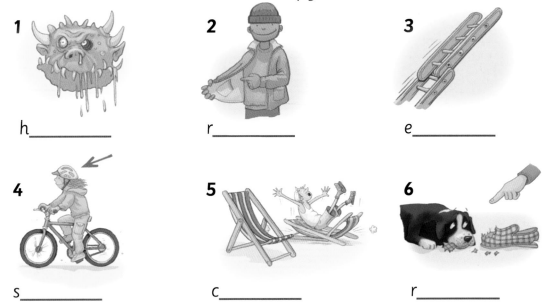

1 h_____

2 r_____

3 e_____

4 s_____

5 c_____

6 r_____

B Write a sentence describing the labelled picture
at the top of the page.

Using words

A Add the **ible** suffix to these words.

   1 access + ible = _____   **2** convert + ible = _____

   3 digest + ible = _____   **4** destruct + ible = _____

> Watch out when you add the **ible** suffix to a word ending in one **e**. Usually you need to drop the **e** and then add the suffix.

B Add the **ible** suffix to these words ending in **e**.

   1 sense + ible = _____   **2** reverse + ible = _____

   3 response + ible = _____   **4** collapse + ible = _____

Puzzle corner

Some words imply smallness.
These words are called **diminutives**.
Diminutives have special suffixes like et, ette, kin, ling and ock.

A Write these words with their diminutive.

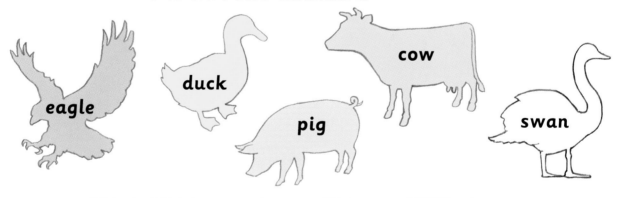

eagle   duck   cow   pig   swan

   piglet   cygnet   bullock   eaglet   duckling

B Make a list of diminutives with each of these suffixes.

      et   ette   kin   ling   ock

Unit 17
ive

explosive

massive

attractive	impressive	alternative	disruptive
detective	massive	expensive	distinctive
protective	secretive	explosive	inventive
reflective	talkative	repulsive	progressive

Finding words

A Copy the sentences.
Fill the gaps with a word from the word list.

1 Thomas always gets told off for being t_____!

2 The fireman wears p_____ clothing.

3 The school production of Cinderella was i_____.

4 The d_____ solved the crime.

B Write your own sentence using a different word from the word list.

Using words

A Add the **ive** suffix to each of these words. Remember, if a word ends in **e**, drop the **e** before adding **ive**.

1 attract   **2** secret   **3** defense

4 mass   **5** expense   **6** abuse

7 decorate   **8** collect   **9** destruct

B Write the antonym of the word positive.
Clue: It is an **ive** word.

Do you remember... an **antonym** is a word with the opposite meaning to another word?

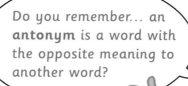

Puzzle corner

Many different words can be made from root words by adding prefixes.

Each of the words below can be made into two new words by adding two of the prefixes in the box.

un   dis   mis   re   anti   ex

like   take
lay   social   claim

Can you make the ten new words?

Unit 18
ie
ei

weight

shriek

chief	eight	believe	ceiling
thief	weight	priest	deceive
belief	sleigh	relieve	receive
relief	weigh	shriek	receipt

Finding words

A Look at the picture.
There are six **ie** or **ei** words
that can be found in the picture.
Write the six words.

All of the words can be found in the word list.

Paid in Full

B Write about the picture using the words you have found.

Using words

Spelling words with **ie** or **ei** can be tricky, but there is a rule to remember that can help...

    p**ie**ce   rec**ei**ve   r**ei**gn

Say the rule a few times aloud; it really helps with your spelling if you can remember it.

*i comes before e except after **c**, or when the sound is not **ee**.*

A Add **ie** or **ei** to these letters to make a word to match the picture.

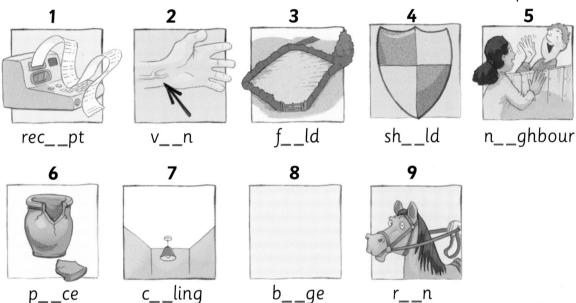

1	2	3	4	5
rec_ _pt	v_ _n	f_ _ld	sh_ _ld	n_ _ghbour

6	7	8	9
p_ _ce	c_ _ling	b_ _ge	r_ _n

B Check each of the words in a dictionary, to check you have spelt them correctly.

Puzzle corner

Rewrite this short passage.
Spell all the words correctly!
Underline the words you change.

Have you managed to spot all nine spelling mistakes?

    A loud niegh came from the stables.
    Liam ran to his hoarse to check everythink was all right.
    As he terned the corner, he spoted a fire.
    Quickly, he led his horse by the riens to saftey.
    The fire brigade arrived befor too much damage had bean done.

tion

investigation

emo**tion**	ac**tion**	atten**tion**	celebra**tion**
lo**tion**	direc**tion**	inven**tion**	conserva**tion**
mo**tion**	frac**tion**	men**tion**	examina**tion**
po**tion**	subtrac**tion**	preven**tion**	investiga**tion**

Finding words

A Copy the sentences.
Fill the gaps with a word from the word list.

1 The ____ of the train made Harry feel sick!

2 Only a ____ of the cake was left.

3 The green ____ bubbled as the toad was added.

4 Uncle James's wedding was a real ____.

B Write your own sentence using a different word from the word list.

Using words

A Copy the sentences and find the rhyming words in the box!

eruption	station
intention	situation
completion	position
subtraction	potion

1 **location** rhymes with _____
2 **addition** rhymes with _____
3 **deletion** rhymes with _____
4 **lotion** rhymes with _____
5 **attraction** rhymes with _____
6 **celebration** rhymes with _____
7 **disruption** rhymes with _____
8 **invention** rhymes with _____

B Write three sentences, each with a gap where a **tion** word is needed. Test your teacher! See if she or he can fill the gaps correctly.

Puzzle corner

Do you know when to use **its** or **it's**?

Use **its** when something belongs to something.
Use **it's** in place of it is or it has.

Copy the sentences and fill the gaps with **its** or **it's**.

_____ a very wet day.

Shall we work on our invention?

We need to decide on _____ colour before we show anyone.

I love the way _____ buttons flash.

So do I! I just hope _____ good enough and wins the competition.

Unit 20
sion

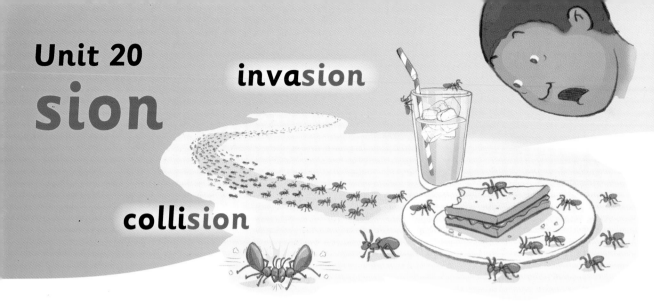

invasion

collision

colli**sion**	aggre**ssion**	abra**sion**	concu**ssion**
deci**sion**	expre**ssion**	inva**sion**	discu**ssion**
divi**sion**	impre**ssion**	occa**sion**	percu**ssion**
televi**sion**	profe**ssion**	persua**sion**	repercu**ssion**

Finding words

A Look at the pictures.
Find the word in the word list and copy it.

B Write a sentence describing the labelled
picture at the top of the page.

Using words

A Copy the table.
Sort the words in the box into the table.

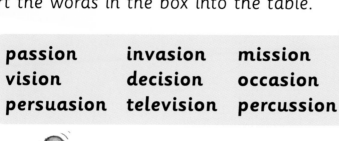

passion	invasion	mission
vision	decision	occasion
persuasion	television	percussion

ision	asion	ssion

B Write down three more **sion** words.
Do any of them fit into the table above?

Puzzle corner

Homophones are words that sound the same but have different spellings.

Challenge... Can you write a sentence that includes all the homophones in each box?

1   **there**   **their**   **they're**

2   **your**   **you're**

3   **whose**   **who's**

Hint – If you aren't sure about the different meanings of the words, check them in a dictionary.

43

Unit 21
wa

waterfall

swan

walk	wallet	swallow	wardrobe
wand	walnut	swamp	warren
wasp	walrus	swarm	warrior
water	watch	swan	waterfall

Finding words

A Look at the picture.
There are eleven **wa** words that can be found in the picture.
Write the eleven words.

All of the words can be found in the word list.

B Write about the picture using at least six of the words you have found.

Using words

Say the **wa** words aloud.
Do you notice the **wa** makes a different sound in some of the words?

A Copy and sort the words from the box into the table.

| wafer | waffle | waltz | wavy | wake |
| wattle | waterproof | waste | wages | walrus |

wa as in **wa**sp	**wa** as in **wa**ve

B Add one more word to each column in the table.

Puzzle corner

Many different words can be made from root words by adding suffixes.

Each of the words below can be made into new words by adding the suffixes in the box.

| ly | ful | less | ness | ship | hood | tion |

Can you make ten new words?

sad   knight

operate   child   love

friend   pain

Unit 22

ss

assembly   class

class	assist	address	assembly
cross	hassle	embarrass	glossary
guess	missile	harness	necessary
press	vessel	success	possession

Finding words

A What am I?

1 I'm not very happy!

2 Horses wear me.

3 I'm often found at the back of a book and I explain words.

4 I am where you live.

5 I am a container.

6 I'm an anxious or shy feeling.

Hint… You will find the words in the word list!

B Write clues for three more **ss** words. Try them out on a friend.

Using words

A Find six double **ss** words in this wordsearch.

d	h	g	u	e	s	s
g	u	b	t	k	f	t
l	c	l	a	s	s	a
a	e	o	b	i	f	k
s	d	r	e	s	s	i
s	b	i	d	a	o	s
c	o	m	p	a	s	s

B Now write each word ending in **ss** in its plural form.

Do you remember... if you need to write a noun ending in **ss** in its plural form, you need to add **es**?

Puzzle corner

A Copy these words and underline the root word.

   1 sunny   **2** singer   **3** agreeable

B Challenge! Explain why you think the root words were used in each of these words.

Like this...

helpful

The root word **help** is used because it is a way of describing the **help** someone gives.

Spelling Challenge

Write a word that uses each of these sounds or letter patterns.

You have practised all the sounds and letter patterns in this book!

1 less, ness
2 er
3 al
4 ment
5 hood, ship
6 on, en
7 rr, ll
8 ic
9 un, re, non, dis
10 ending in f
11 ight
12 ory, ery, ary
13 ough
14 able
15 ible
16 ive
17 ie, ei
18 tion
19 sion
20 wa
21 ss

Well done, you have now finished this book. We hope it has helped you with your spellings.